US Armored Cars

in action

By Jim Mesko

Color by Don Greer

**Illustrated by Ernesto Cumpian
and David W. Smith**

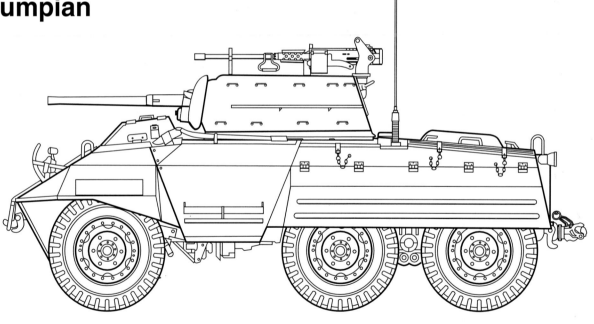

Armor Number 37

squadron/signal publications

(Cover) An M8 of Combat Command B, 7th Armored Division fires on German positions in support of A Company, 23rd Infantry Regiment in August of 1944. The action took place near Epernay, east of Chateau Thierry near the Marne River.

Acknowledgements

US Army
National Archives
Patton Armor Museum
Mike Green
Dave Spenser
...and a very special thanks to Wayne Hlavin who not only let me photograph his M20 in great detail, but also gave me a ride in it. Thanks also go to Sergeant Joel Block of the Albuquerque Police Department who took time out from his busy schedule to show me his department's V-100 armored cars one very hot Saturday afternoon.

Dedication:

This book is dedicated to the memory of Nick Waters, III, and Jack Weaver who both passed away this year. Both were good friends who contributed greatly to modeling. Nick was the editor at Squadron/Signal Publications for ten years and we worked on a lot of books together. He was also a founder of the Small Air Forces Observer, a Navy veteran, and an active member of IPMS. Jack was a longtime friend from my early days in the Cleveland IPMS and he and his wife Marge were like a second pair of parents to me. A consistent winner at the IPMS Nationals, his modeling standard were superb and greatly influenced me. Their passing leaves all who knew them with a great loss. May they rest in peace.

ISBN 0-89747-391-4

If you have any photographs of aircraft, armor, soldiers or ships of any nation, particularly wartime snapshots, why not share them with us and help make Squadron/Signal's books all the more interesting and complete in the future. Any photograph sent to us will be copied and the original returned. The donor will be fully credited for any photos used. Please send them to:

Squadron/Signal Publications, Inc.
1115 Crowley Drive
Carrollton, TX 75011-5010

Если у вас есть фотографии самолётов, вооружения, солдат или кораблей любой страны, особенно, снимки времён войны, поделитесь с нами и помогите сделать новые книги издательства Эскадрон/Сигнал ещё интереснее. Мы переснимем ваши фотографии и вернём оригиналы. Имена приславших снимки будут сопровождать все опубликованные фотографии. Пожалуйста, присылайте фотографии по адресу:

Squadron/Signal Publications, Inc.
1115 Crowley Drive
Carrollton, TX 75011-5010

軍用機、装甲車両、兵士、軍艦などの写真を所持しておられる方はいらっしゃいませんか？どの国のものでも結構です。作戦中に撮影されたものが特に良いのです。Squadron/Signal社の出版する刊行物において、このような写真は内容を一層充実し、興味深くすることができます。当方にお送り頂いた写真は、複写の後お返しいたします。出版物中に写真を使用した場合は、必ず提供者のお名前を明記させて頂きます。お写真は下記にご送付ください。

Squadron/Signal Publications, Inc.
1115 Crowley Drive
Carrollton, TX 75011-5010

(Right) The M8 first saw service in Italy in early 1944. ARGONAUGHT, an M8 from the 91st Cavalry Reconnaissance, was near Cassino in February or March of 1944. The markings on the bow are unusual for a vehicle in a forward combat zone. The raised position of the .50 caliber machine gun optimized the weapon for use against aircraft while keeping the gunner under the protection of the turret armor. (US Army)

ARGONAUGHT

5A9IR A49

Introduction

The armored car has held a unique position within the armed forces of the United States. Unlike most major military powers, the US military has never really fostered the development of the armored car to any great degree except during World War Two. The attitude toward armored cars can be attributed to two schools of thought — one military and one industrial. The overall military view is that a tracked vehicle, with its superior mobility, can do a better job than an armored car. Although tracked vehicles are more expensive, the great wealth of the US makes such a view acceptable. The second argument relates to the large automotive industry within America. This vast manufacturing base has allowed the US military the luxury of using existing engines, power trains, and chassis to build armored cars as the need arose. While this has led to some problems, such as false starts and wasted time and money, it has also shown that it can work.

The start of the American armored car program can be traced back to 1898 when Colonel Royal P. Davidson fitted a Duryea automobile chassis with a Colt machine gun and a small armored shield. Over the next ten years, Davidson modified seven other automobiles into armored cars, culminating in a drive from Chicago to San Francisco to demonstrate their military potential. While Davidson's work did not lead to major changes in US military mechanization, it did earn him the title "Father of the American Armored Car."

Although Davidson's efforts did trigger some interest in armored cars in the United States, no concerted development program began. Instead, a variety of commercial vehicles were modified for this purpose. During the Mexican border dispute in 1916 (which resulted from the raid on Columbus, New Mexico by Pancho Villa) US army troops under General John J. Pershing deployed, first along the border, then into Mexico after Villa. Several modified commercial vehicles including the Jeffrey Quad, the 1916 White Armored Car, and others manufactured by Mack, Locomobile, and Ford went with US troops into Mexico. These vehicles saw little, if any, action and mainly served to bolster the morale of the populace and dampen lawlessness in some of the more isolated towns along the border.

The US entry into World War One did little to change the overall attitude towards the armored car in the United States. During the nine years following the cessation of hostilities, there were no official programs underway. Then, in 1927, work began on a variety of vehicles based on commercial cars and trucks starting with the T1 that was little changed from Davidson's initial Duryea modification. Later vehicles progressed through various models, but none were designed from the ground up as an armored car.

Then in 1931, Cunningham Motors of Rochester, New York built two armored cars based on newly issued US Army Ordnance Department specifications. Designated the T4, the vehicles had six road wheels (four powered) with a low mounted spare behind the front wheels. These spares could rotate and were used to help the T4 over road obstructions which might come in contact with the chassis. The T4 was nearly sixteen feet long and carried one .30 and one .50 caliber machine gun in a rear mounted turret. The army liked what it saw and ordered an additional twenty vehicles produced at the Rock Island Arsenal, Illinois. The vehicles were redesignated M1 armored cars and saw service throughout the 1930s.

The T4/M1 was followed by a series of smaller vehicles, including the wheeled or tracked T5, and the T7 based on a Franklin truck chassis. The T7 was part of a series of prototypes built by the Holabird Quartermaster Depot in Maryland which included the T6, T8, T9, and T10. Only the T7 was built beyond a single prototype with six being produced. These were followed by the T11. Seven T11se were procured and one served as a test-bed for the T11E1 and T11E2.

Various US commercial firms, however, designed armored vehicles for the foreign market. These included Marmon-Herrington which had produced the T11 for France, the American Armament Corporation, and auto designer Preston Tucker. While a few foreign governments such as China and Persia (current day Iran) purchased some vehicles, there were no large scale orders nor were there any radical changes in design or construction.

When World War Two erupted in Europe in September of 1939, there was little in the way of an American armored car program. The closest thing to an armored car in large scale production was the White M3 Scout Car. Derived from the T7 Scout Car, this design had matured through a series of models and would eventually evolve into the M2/M3 Halftrack. Although

The T4 was the first American armored car designed from the ground up for this role. The T4 was an advanced vehicle with a powerful engine, four wheel drive, good speed, and a large radius of action. Additional brackets on the turret held extra machine guns. (PAM)

One of the earliest US armored car designs was the Trackless Tank. The vehicle featured eight wheels mounted on a Christie suspension. The vehicle lacked the necessary ruggedness on the battlefield and the project was terminated. (PAM)

the M3 did see some service in the Mediterranean in the traditional armored car role, it remained primarily a utility vehicle and it did not see extensive front-line use with the US Army.

The first serious project that resulted from the emergency plan for rearmament was the so-called 'Trackless Tank' designed and built by the Trackless Tank Corporation of New York. The ten-ton Diesel-powered vehicle had eight evenly spaced wheels mounted on a Christie-type suspension. The rear six wheels were powered while the front pair were used for steering. It was planned to use the basic chassis as a mobile gun platform for the tank destroyer, artillery, and anti-aircraft roles. Unfortunately, the design was too fragile for battlefield use and only one was built. The Trackless Tank served as the basis for the T13 which featured a cleaner outline, a turret, and welded construction versus the riveted Trackless Tank. While the T13 was marginally a better vehicle, it still lacked the ruggedness required on the battlefield and only two prototypes were produced.

By mid-1941 the American armored car program began to take a number of divergent courses based on size, mission requirements, and input from British experiences on the battlefields of Europe and North Africa. During the summer of 1941 the Ordnance Department, working with the British Tank Mission, laid down requirements for light, medium, and heavy classes of armored cars. British influence, driven by experience from the fighting in North Africa, was apparent in the medium and heavy classes. Consequently, the main thrust of the US armored car program focused on the light class of vehicles.

In July of 1941 requirements were formulated for a Gun Motor Carriage for the new Tank Destroyer Command. The vehicle was to have high speed and cross country mobility, six wheel drive, a low silhouette, low weight, and a 37mm gun. Additionally the vehicle was to be convertible into mortar carrier, anti-aircraft, and munitions carrier variants. During the fall of 1941 two companies, Ford and the Fargo Division of Chrysler, were given contracts to develop a 37mm Gun Motor Carriage under the designations T22 and T23 respectively. Studebaker also became involved when they offered to build their own privately funded vehicle under the designation T43 (later changed to the T21). This led to another set of contracts issued to Ford and Chrysler for four-wheeled versions of their basic designs under the designations T22E1 and T23E1.

The idea of using the 37mm cannon in the anti-tank role soon proved to be impractical. Battlefield experience in North Africa had demonstrated that the smaller weapon was no longer viable in the anti-tank role. Nevertheless, there was still a need for a light armored vehicle by the Tank Destroyer Command and the Army's Cavalry Reconnaissance units. As a result, the vehicles under study had their designation changed from Gun Motor Carriage to light armored car.

Tests showed the Ford T22 to have the best overall design and performance although numerous modifications were requested. These included improving the visibility from the driving compartment hatches, eliminating the .30 caliber hull machine gun, adding armored storage boxes and removable side skirts over the wheels, and internal changes for stowage and radio equipment. These modifications led to the vehicle being redesignated the T22E2. After further testing the vehicle was deemed acceptable for service on 19 May 1942 and assigned the production designation M8 Light Armored Car. The British named the M8 the Greyhound, although the name never really caught on with US forces. The adoption of the M8 resulted in the cancellation of the six-wheeled T23 and the four-wheeled T22E1 and T23E1. Tests on the Studebaker T21, however, continued into the fall of 1942. While it proved to be a good vehicle, it was no better than the M8 and it too was canceled in December of that year.

By mid-1941 the Ordnance Department decided on three classes of armored cars — light, medium, and heavy. Only the light class of vehicles would see US service during WW II and three companies eventually became involved in the program: Studebaker with the T21, Ford with the T22, and Chrysler with the T23. The Studebaker T21 was offered by the company as a private venture. All three vehicles bore an amazing resemblance to each other. (PAM)

The eventual winner of the competition was the Ford T22. Some minor faults were corrected and the modified vehicle, now the T22E2, was accepted for production in May of 1942 as the M8 Light Armored Car. The main armament was a 37mm gun mounted in an open-topped turret. A .50 caliber machine gun could be mounted on the turret rear for anti-aircraft use and close-in protection. (PAM)

Development

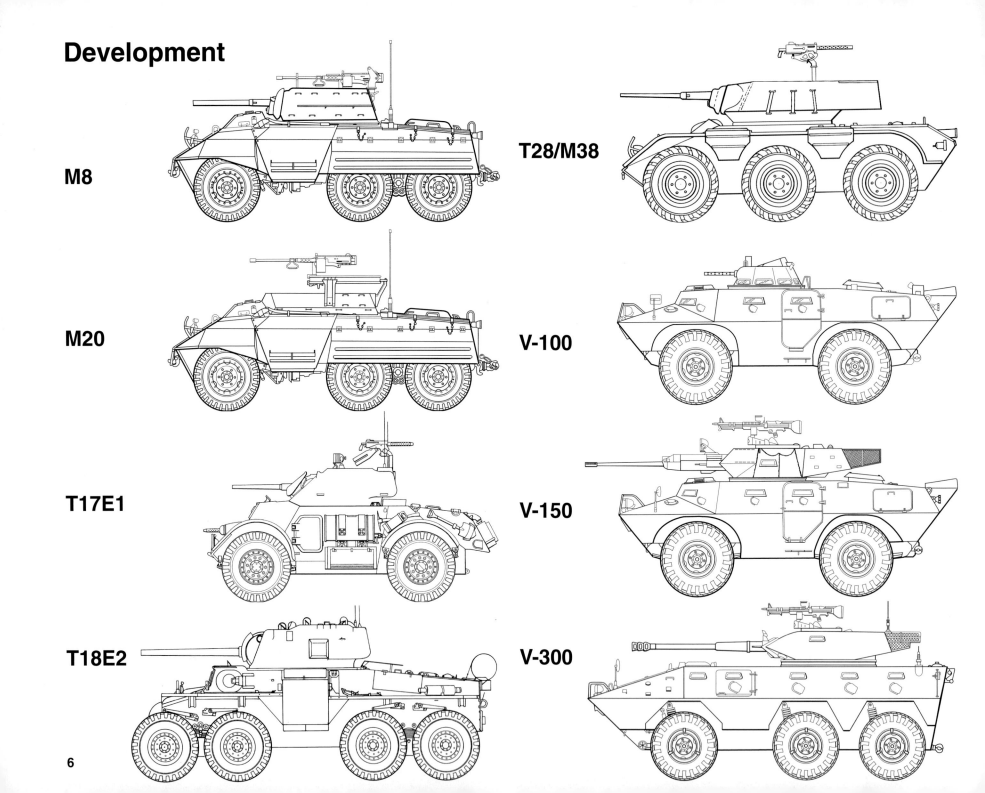

M8

M20

T17E1

T18E2

T28/M38

V-100

V-150

V-300

M8 Armored Car

The M8 was a six-wheeled armored car armed with a 37mm cannon in an open-topped turret. A co-axial .30 caliber machine gun was mounted in line with the 37mm gun on the right. Both weapons were mounted in an M6 gun mount. A .50 caliber machine gun could be fitted to a pintle mount at the turret rear. Later many vehicles had an M49 ring mount installed over the turret to improve the machine gun's field of fire. Some of the vehicles were modified in the field while others were modified in rear area depots. The M8 had originally been envisioned as a vehicle for the Tank Destroyer Force, but by the time it entered service the 37mm cannon lacked the necessary punch to deal with all but the lightest armored vehicles. The weapon was still useful against soft skinned vehicles and ground troops when firing high explosive, armor piercing, and canister rounds.

The hull was of all-welded construction and was divided into three sections — driver's, turret, and engine compartments. The driver and assistant driver sat under a raised box-like structure which had a two part hatch on top that folded out toward the side on top and a front flap that folded forward. Vision ports were in the sides and flaps, but when buttoned up visibility was severely restricted. There was also a Protecto-scope on the forward flap, similar in size to the direct vision port. A conventional steering wheel controlled the front wheels. The driver had the option of four forward and two reverse gears and could use a high or low gear range for road travel or rough terrain.

The 37mm open topped gun turret was mounted over the fighting compartment immediately behind the drivers' compartments. The turret was hand traversed through 360 degrees via a single speed handwheel. Later models featured a two-speed system. The gun was hand elevated from -10 to +20 degrees. Eighty rounds of 37mm ammunition were carried in racks on the turret wall and in bins in the fighting compartment. The vehicle commander and gunner sat on seats attached to the turret ring and rotated with the turret.

The M8 was not heavily armored, although it made good use of angled plates to get the best protection possible and still keep the vehicle's weight down. The revised drivers' positions featured two-piece hatches which folded forward in front and to the side on the top. The mirror on the fender was not used on production models. (PAM)

The M8 was powered by a 110-horsepower, 320 cubic inch Hercules JXD six-cylinder engine. The vehicle featured all wheel drive via separate shafts from the transfer case. Just forward of the engine was a 54 gallon gas tank which provided a range of 100-250 miles over rough terrain or 200-400 miles on roads. Maximum highway speed was around 60 MPH while cross country performance was between 40-55 MPH. The radiator was mounted at the rear with

(Above) The T22E2 was very close in its final layout to the original T22, differing only in the revised driver's compartment and the elimination of the hull machine gun. The addition of the side skirts cosmetically altered the vehicle's appearance, but had little effect on protection or performance. The production M8 differed little from the T22E2. (PAM)

(Below) The M8 was equipped with a 37mm cannon and M6 mount in a circular open-topped turret. The driver was in the left front portion of the hull with his assistant to the right. The gunner/commander sat on the left side of the turret with the loader in the right. This vehicle lacks the machine gun mount on the rear of the turret. The large rectangular shapes on the rear deck are the engine access hatches. (PAM)

A large set of louvers helped to cool the M8's engine compartment. A trailer towing hitch was mounted below the louvers. Most M8s had heavy gauge wire rods spot welded to the turret side to hold canvas or leather stowage straps in place. Wire or rope to hold camouflage was also strung through the rods. The turret machine gun has been locked into its stowage rack with the breech and handgrips protruding through the pintle. (PAM)

two belt-driven fans for additional cooling. Access was gained through two doors on the rear deck. The doors opened toward the center and were held in place by single prop rods.

The hull was equipped with side skirts that could fold up or be removed to clean accumulated dirt and mud from the wheels and hull side. Their removal drastically altered the outline of the vehicle. Early M8s had a rack for three mines between the front and middle set of tires. The rack was sometimes replaced by a field modified jerry can rack. Later, storage bins replaced the mine racks. An additional set of stowage bins was placed over the middle and rear wheels on both sides of the hull. Additional personal equipment could also be stored on the turret side rails. A towing pintle was mounted at the lower rear hull for a small trailer, although this was normally used only in rear areas or during road travel.

This M8, possibly a pre-production test vehicle, has been fitted with mounts for both a .30 and .50 caliber machine gun for a publicity display. The .50 caliber machine gun's telescoping pintle mount allowed higher angles of fire against aircraft while still keeping the gunner under armor protection. The mount seems to have been rarely used. Later an M49 machine gun ring mount was added to the M8 turret to improve the horizontal field of fire for the machine gun. (PAM)

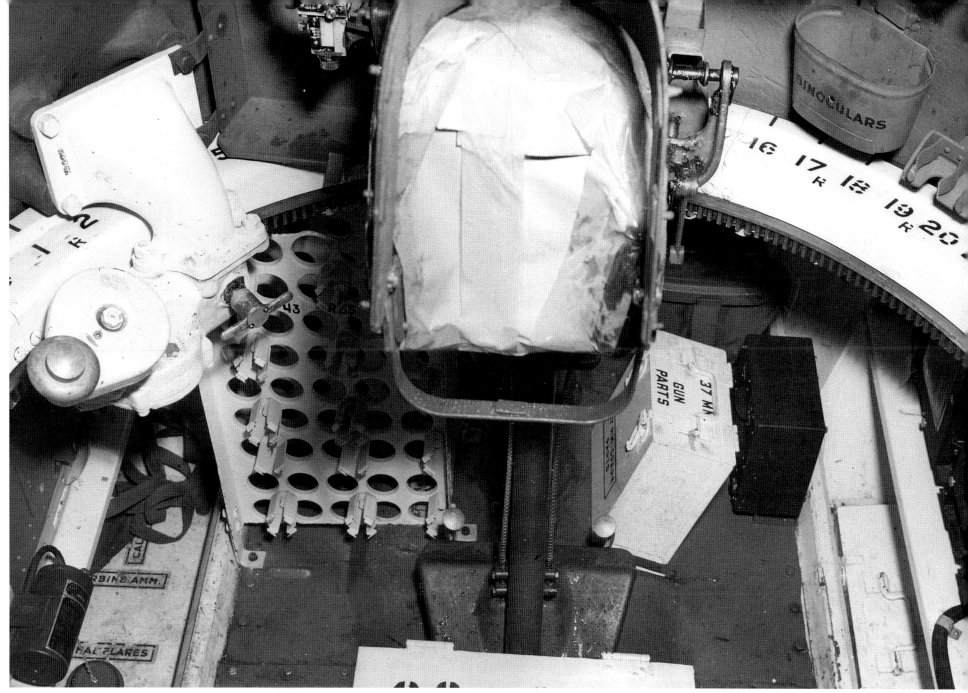

The 37mm gun turret was not much roomier, even when fitted with a revised ammunition storage arrangement. The knob on the left is the two-speed traverse gear. To its right is the recoil guard and covered breech of the 37mm cannon. Two small foot operated buttons on the small platform directly below the breech fire the guns. The button on the left fires the main gun, while the right button fires the co-axial machine gun. Either the gunner or loader could fire the weapons. (US Army)

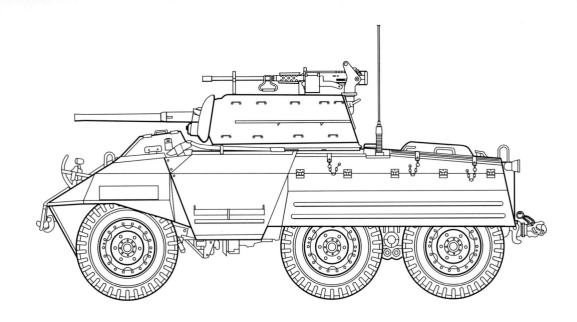

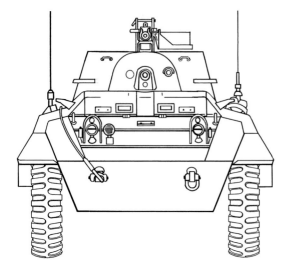

M8 Armored Car Specifications

Length...............16 Feet, 5 Inches
Width.................8 Feet, 4 Inches
Height................7 Feet, 4.5 Inches
Weight...............17,200 Pounds
Armament..........1 x 37mm gun, 1 x .30 caliber coaxial machine gun, 1 x pintle mounted .30 caliber machine gun.
Speed.................56 MPH
Crew....................4

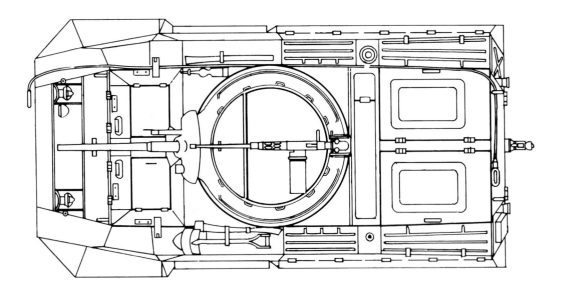

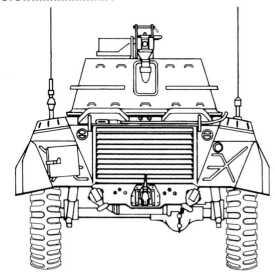

M20 Armored Utility Car

When the T22 project was started, it was specified that the vehicle was to be easily modified to fill a number of different roles. When the T22 was accepted for production as the M8, the Ordnance Department, at the request of the Tank Destroyer Force, initiated modifications for a general command and cargo vehicle. Ford carried out the work and the revised vehicle, designated the T26 Armored Utility Vehicle, was accepted for service use. When it was accepted for production, it was redesignated the M10 Armored Utility Vehicle, but to avoid confusion with the new M10 Gun Motor Carriage, the designation was changed again to M20.

The M20 was an M8 with the turret removed and a low, box-like open topped superstructure added over the fighting compartment in its place. An M49 ring mount and .50 caliber machine gun were fitted over the enlarged fighting compartment. Bench seats were added on each side of the fighting compartment providing seating for four passengers. Another seat was provided at the rear for the gunner, while a folding map table was mounted at the front for the commander. Internally, the side storage bins were modified and provisions were made for carbine weapon racks and a bazooka. The loss of the turret and 37mm gun reduced the vehicle's weight by about one ton, resulting in slightly improved performance over the turreted M8.

M20 Observations

I had a chance to closely examine and ride in a restored M20 owned by Wayne Hlavin of Medina, Ohio. Wayne is a military vehicle collector who runs an annual display and reenactment day on the third weekend in July. I found his M20 to be only slightly larger than my 1995 four-door Ford Explorer — most notably in width. The drivers' compartments were a close fit even for my relatively small frame and, when the hatches were shut, there was very little headroom. This probably explains why most photos of M8s and M20s in the field have both hatches open. Buttoned up, the visibility from either position was extremely limited and I would not have wanted to drive it this way. Even with the hatches open, Wayne needed me to spot for him when we took the vehicle out onto the highway.

What really impressed me, however, was how the vehicle performed. We took it out for a

drive over a series of rough trails on his farm and I was very surprised by its smooth ride. By comparison, a later ride in an M3 Halftrack was far rougher and much noisier. At one point we were traveling between 30 and 40 MPH and the ride was still fairly smooth even over the rough ground. When we took it out onto the main road, the ride was little different from any other vehicle. We moved along at a fairly good speed along a country lane, and the Walter Mitty in me had visions of France during the summer of 1944. When we returned, instead of backing into the parking space he just came in from behind and crossed over the railroad ties with hardly a noticeable bump.

I was really impressed with my ride in the M20. The vehicle had good speed, handled well, and provided a smooth ride, particularly on roads. All these attributes must have been appreciated by the crews when they took the vehicle into combat. On the downside, the cramped drivers' area and limited visibility were enough to make me never to have wanted to be there in combat. Overall, I came away impressed with the vehicle and with a better understanding of what it must have been like to operate. A special thanks to Wayne for being so generous with his time and vehicle.

M8 Armored Car

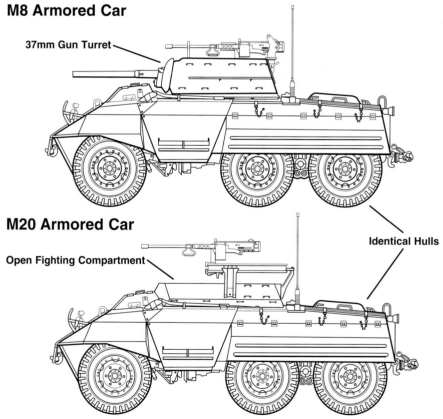

(Left) The M20 was nearly identical to the M8 except for the 37mm gun turret. The prototype T26 had a ring mount for a .50 caliber machine gun in place of the 37mm cannon. Both vehicles used the same Technical Manual. (PAM)

The ring mount on the T26 was simplified with the upper sides being removed and the M49 ring mount being supported by three metal arms — one on each side and one at the back. This vehicle has the drivers' front hatches opened and windshields fitted into the openings. (PAM)

At least one M20 was fitted with a twin .50 caliber machine gun mount. The twin mount was designed to provide heavy fire support for infantry, but was not officially adopted. This vehicle has all four drivers' compartment hatches open — a normal configuration unless the crew was under fire. (PAM)

The ring mount extended slightly over the rear of the fighting compartment, which resulted in a pronounced step in the rear support arm. This vehicle has replaced the mine rack with an additional stowage bin between the first and second wheel. (PAM)

When closed up, the driver's view was restricted to what was visible through the direct vision slot on the left and the Protecto-scope on the right. The hatches were normally left open unless it was absolutely necessary to close them. From the author's personal experience, this was not a job for someone with claustrophobia. (Mesko)

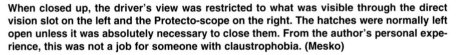

12

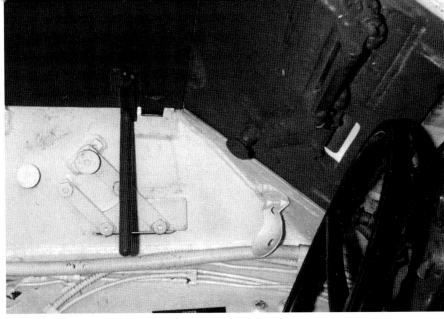

When closed up, the driver's compartment was cramped and the view limited. The 'L' shaped upper hatch handle is directly in front of the direct vision slot on the side. The handle was normally swung up and back. (Mesko)

(Right) The driver sat on the left side of the vehicle and the layout of the position was fairly standard. While it is not evident, both the driver and assistant driver's positions were extremely cramped. The inner surfaces of the driver's hatches were painted olive drab with the remainder of the interior painted white. The steering wheel was a semi-gloss black. (Mesko)

The driver and assistant driver sat under two-piece hatches. The upper hatch opened to the side, while the front hatch opened to the front. A Protecto-scope was fitted toward the center, while a direct vision slot was placed to the outside of the hatch. The direct vision slot could be closed off by the sliding shutter. The long bar welded to the bottom of the hatch provided leverage to pull the hatch closed. (Mesko)

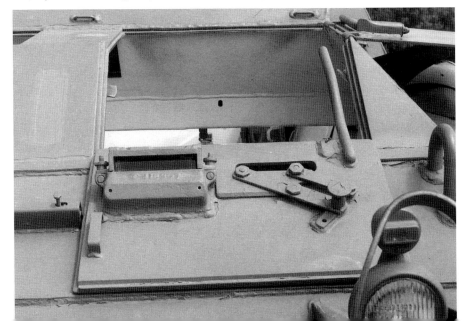

(Right) The upper hatch folded outward and could be pulled back using the 'L' shaped pivoting metal rod. These photos are of M20 hatches which are identical to those found on the M8. The white interior greatly improved the interior lighting conditions when the vehicle was buttoned up. (Mesko)

The M49 Ring Mount provided a 360 degree arc of fire and was very stable. The ring mount was bolted onto the support arms and the pintle skated around the ring using a series of horizontal and vertical rollers. The sides and front of the M20's parapet are joined with a rather prominent weld bead. (Mesko)

The gun mount was able to pivot through a 360 degree arc. When properly maintained, the machine gun moved easily on the ring mount and could be brought to bear on a target in seconds. (Mesko)

The M20's open fighting compartment was equipped with wooden bench seats along the hull sides. Radio and equipment bins were built into the sponsons behind the seats. A smaller wooden seat was attached to the rear bulkhead for the machine gunner. (Mesko)

Both the machine gun and its mount can be secured so that there is no danger of the gun swinging around freely when not in use. The weapon has a satin black finish and the wooden hand grips and cocking handle are stained a dark brown. The .50 caliber machine gun rounds are inert, as denoted by the holes in the cartridge cases. (Mesko)

The sponson compartments were quite large, and when not used for radio equipment, held a large amount of ammunition and personal gear. (Mesko)

Early Fixed Pintle Mount

The interior sponson compartments on the left side were divided in half horizontally and folded outward. A wide variety of radios could be carried including the SCR-510, SCR-506, SCR-508, and the SCR-694-C. (Mesko)

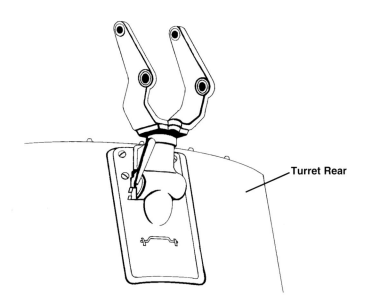

Turret Rear

The tires were pneumatic 'combat' types with a non-directional tread. The tires are fitted on a divided rim and are held in place by an outer lock rim. The tire pressure on the front tires was 60 psi, while the rear tires were 50 psi. (Mesko)

There were two stowage boxes on each side of the hull running the length of the rear fender. The rearmost bins were longer and had a 'V' shaped reinforcing strip underneath the bin's lid. The shorter bins had a single strip running from one upper corner to the other lower corner (Mesko)

A small mine rack was located on each side of the vehicle between the front and middle wheels. The rack held three mines. Later vehicles had the racks replaced by a pair of conformal stowage bins. Some vehicles had also replaced the mine rack with a rack for a pair of jerry cans. In hindsight there is a certain irony in stenciling 'STEP HERE' on a rack full of mines... (Mesko)

Jerry Can Rack

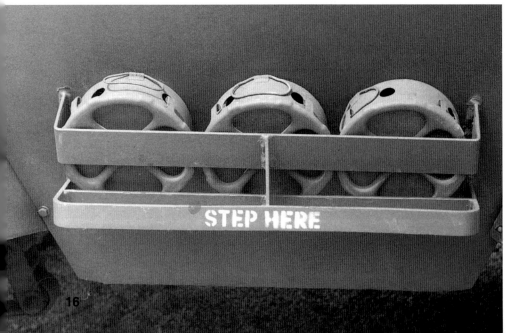

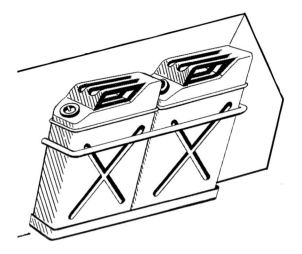

Two large vent covers on the rear deck provided access to the engine compartment. The covers were hinged along the vehicle's center line and were equipped with tie downs used to secure extra gear. (Mesko)

The opened engine vent covers were held in place with a prop rod. The covers were vented to draw air in over the engine. The inner surface of the lids was painted olive drab. The interior of the engine compartment was generally white. (Mesko)

Armored Gas Cap Cover (Closed)

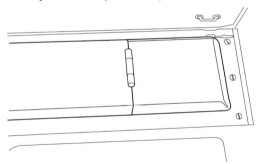

Armored Gas Cap Cover (Open)

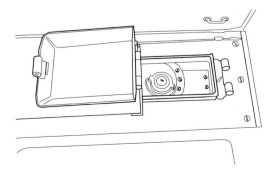

The M8 and M20 were powered by a 110 hp Hercules JXD engine. The carburetor, exhaust manifold, and intake manifold were mounted on the engine's left side. The thermostat housing and the radiator hose were mounted on the engine's right side. The vehicle fuel tank is mounted directly in front of the engine. (Mesko)

17

The engine was cooled by two fans placed between the engine and the radiator. Cooling air was pulled into the engine compartment via the vented hatches on the engine deck and pushed out through the radiator and armored louvers at the rear of the vehicle. The cooling fans were connected to the generator with a serpentine rubber belt. (Mesko)

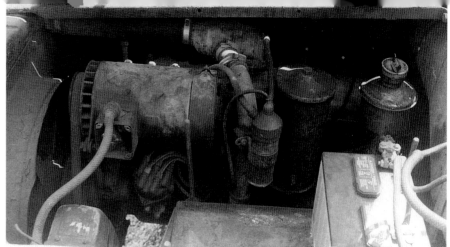

The right side of the engine bay contained the generator, distributor, ignition coil, and the cylindrical oil filter canister. The oil filler cap is on the crankcase breather next to the battery. (Mesko)

Engine (Right Side)

Engine (Left Side)

The M8 and M20 in Service

The first M8s began rolling off the production line in March of 1943, but it took some time for the vehicles to reach the combat zones. The M8 first appeared in the Mediterranean Theater of Operations (MTO) after the Allies invaded the Italian mainland at Salerno on 9 September 1943. Once introduced, they gradually began to replace the older M3 Scout Cars being used in Cavalry and Reconnaissance units. The slow moving and often static nature of the fighting in the rugged Italian countryside severely limited their employment and they saw little use in their intended role.

By the time the Allies hit the beaches in Normandy in June of 1944, the M8 had become the primary vehicle of the Reconnaissance platoons' armored car sections. Each section was composed of three M8s. The M8s were used to support the platoon's three Scout Squads each of which had two jeeps. This gave the platoon a very flexible structure since the two elements could be used in various combinations as the need arose. Even though the 37mm gun of the M8 lacked the necessary punch to deal with heavier German armor, the weapon was still useful in providing fire support against dug in infantry and lighter German vehicles.

OPERATION COBRA, the breakout from the Normandy beachhead in late July of 1944, saw the first use of the M8 in its intended role. The US Armored Divisions' reconnaissance troops ranged far ahead of the main columns, probing for weak spots and disrupting the German retreat whenever and wherever possible. The M20 was used in a utility role by the recon units and headquarters sections. The high speed of both vehicles made them difficult targets and allowed them to quickly back away from danger when the Germans turned to make a stand. The first sign of liberation for many towns and villages in occupied France was a section of M8s from a Cavalry Recon unit moving down their streets.

As the Allied advance during the summer and early fall of 1944 gradually subsided and the front began to stabilize, the Cavalry units found themselves being used as mobile security units along division flanks — a job for which they were not really suited. This was to prove all too true during the "Battle of the Bulge" where a number of unsupported Cavalry units were forced to retreat under heavy pressure from German armor. There were even cases of wholesale panic where equipment was prematurely abandoned with little or no fight. At least four M8s of the 18th Cavalry Reconnaissance Squadron, 14th Cavalry Group were abandoned near Poteau and used as a backdrop in one of the most famous series of propaganda photos taken by the Germans in World War Two. Although staged after the initial battles, photos were taken of the Germans attacking, looting, and using the vehicles for shelter.

When the Allies finally contained the German Ardennes offensive and then renewed their own offensive during the early spring of 1945, the M8s were again used to locate enemy strong points and troop concentrations. The crumbling German defenses were often just a hollow shell and once pierced, allowed the Cavalry units to roam the countryside against minimal resistance. During the waning days of the war, M8 sections often accepted the surrender of entire German towns.

Allied employment of the M8 in Europe varied. While various British and Commonwealth units used M8s, its light armor was not well received. Larger, better armored and armed vehicles such as the Staghound were preferred and saw the lion's share of the action. The French, in desperate need of vehicles, received large numbers of both M8s and M20s and used them extensively, particularly with their 2nd Armored Division in their drive to liberate France.

In the Pacific the island hopping nature of the ground war severely limited the usefulness of the armored car. The limited confines of an island, or the rugged mountains of New Guinea,

The crew of NIÑA CHIQUITA takes a break in the rubble filled streets of Gaeta, Italy during May of 1944. The vehicle carries the very conspicuous star and circle markings used from 1943 onward. The markings are likely a dirty white, but may be a fresh yellow. Both colors were used in Sicily and may have been carried onward into Italy. The vehicle also carries a two-tone disruptive camouflage scheme. (US Army)

usually required the services of a slower, but much better armed and armored tank. The M8s were not used in any quantity until the Philippines Campaign and the invasion of Okinawa.

Following the war, large numbers of M8s were supplied to various American allies under different military aid programs. The M8 rapidly became the standard armored car in many rebuilt armored units. Its use in American service declined although it was a favorite vehicle for use in both Occupied Germany and Japan after the war. In June of 1950 North Korea invaded South Korea and both M8s and M20s serving with US forces in Japan were sent to South Korea to help stem the flood of North Korean troops. Combined with a South Korean cavalry unit equipped with 37 M8s, the vehicle was useful in temporarily slowing the North Koreans in some areas and providing vital intelligence on North Korean movements in others. Overall, they were largely ineffective against the North Koreans equipped with T-34/85s and Su-76 self propelled guns and, as the war progressed, the M8s and M20s were gradually relegated to road and base security functions.

The M8's largest combat action after World War Two was with French Union Forces in Indochina. When the 2nd Armored Division arrived for occupation duty, it employed M8s for security duties and road patrols. When the war broke out in 1946, the M8s and other armored vehicles were often limited to the few available roads because of the terrain. They became quick reaction forces responsible for keeping the lines of communication open against communist Viet Minh assaults on convoys and static positions. As the war progressed, this became increasingly dangerous as the Viet Minh often used the initial attack as bait in order to draw the relief force into a prepared ambush. Later in the war the M8s were organized into combined arms reconnaissance units along with tanks and self-propelled howitzers. These units had an armored car troop of three platoons of five M8s each.

When the war ended in a French defeat, a number of M8s were turned over to the newly formed armies of South Vietnam, Laos and Cambodia. In 1957 war began again in South Vietnam. M8s were again used for convoy duty and rear area security, but were gradually replaced by other vehicles as increased American military aid flowed into the country. At least one M8 turret was mounted on an M113 Armored Personnel Carrier in an attempt to augment its firepower, but it appears that it was never used operationally.

The crew of CONQUISTADOR takes a break near the village fountain in Norma, Italy in late May of 1944 as the local villagers look on. The M8 was used during the linkup between Anzio and Salerno during the spring of 1944, although the mountainous Italian countryside was not really suited for mobile forces. (Green)

A US column, led by an M8, passes through the ruins of LaChapelle en Juger, France in late July of 1944 while pursuing retreating German forces. After the US launched OPERATION COBRA, four armored divisions poured through the ruptured German lines with M8s out in front for reconnaissance. The breakout was just the type of mobile campaign for which US forces had trained and they exploited the M8's speed and mobility to bypass German concentrations as they drove across France. (US Army)

The first signs of liberation for many French citizens were M8s who had outflanked German defenses and pushed into the German's rear areas. In this case the citizens of Chartres received a special treat when the commanding general of the 7th Armored Division, Major General Lindsay Sylvester, took part in an impromptu victory parade after the town had been seized by his unit in mid-August. His rank plate, white stars on a red rectangle, is mounted on the right fender above the bridge classification mark. (US Army)

Being out in front did have its dangers and losses did occur. "Sweet Sue", from the Third Army's 42nd Cavalry Reconnaissance Squadron was captured by these German troops during the summer campaign. The trailer was used for additional supplies and ammunition while on the move, but was not normally taken into action. Its presence indicates that the M8 was probably captured in an area the crew thought was secure.

General George S. Patton, Jr. takes the US Ambassador to Russia, Averill Harriman (wearing the older style helmet) on a tour of the Third Army's front in a specially modified M20. Patton's 'customized' vehicle carries his rank and unit plate and a pair of air horns on the glacis plate. A windshield has been added across the front of the parapet and the machine gun ring mount has been removed and replaced with a pintle mount. (Green)

Belgian citizens in the town of Rongy wave at the crew of an M8 who helped liberate their town from the Germans. The M8 has an M49 ring mount added to the turret to improve the .50 caliber machine gun's field of fire. A rack for jerry cans and other stores has replaced the mine rack on the hull side behind the front wheel. (US Army)

An M8 from the 17th Cavalry, Ninth Army rolls past a knocked out Sturmgeschutze III in the rubble strewn town of Kinzweiler, Germany during late November of 1944. The added ring mount, much lower than the mount shown on the upper left photo of page 22, is an indication of the differences which existed with field modifications. (US Army)

The 92nd Cavalry Recon Squadron prepares for an attack from behind the cover of the Maginot Line's battle scarred fortifications. The ring mounts on the M8s have a totally different mounting arrangement than any of those previously shown. The vehicles are missing most or all of their side skirts and are equipped with tire chains. (US Army)

While the opening days of the Battle of the Bulge were snow-free, this quickly changed. The standard US olive drab camouflage stood out starkly against the white background as evidenced by the M8 in the background. The vehicle markings on the lead M8 have been left on the original olive drab background to make them more visible. (US Army)

The crew of this 11th Armored Division M8 greets infantry from the 84th Infantry Division during the final stages of the Battle of the Bulge in mid-January of 1945. Snow chains were widely used by M8s and M20s to improve traction both on and off the road. (US Army)

Antenna Base and Mount

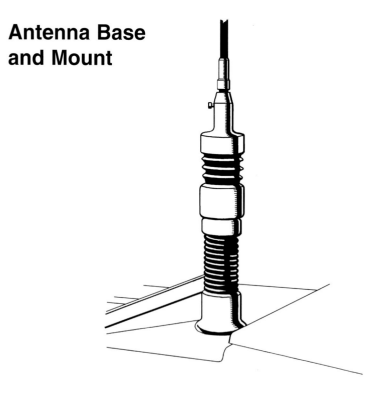

The crew of KANSAS TERROR doesn't seem to be too concerned that they are violating the German "No Stopping or Parking" sign next to their vehicle. "Der Ortskomandant" roughly translates to 'The Locale Commander'. A jury-rigged stowage rack appear to have replaced the pintle mounted machine gun on the turret. (US Army)

RUSTY, an M20 of the 6th Cavalry Squadron of Patton's Third Army moves through a German town in February of 1945. RUSTY appears to be in yellow with all other markings in white. A special, and possibly non-standard, ring mount encircles the fighting compartment. A windshield has also been added to the front of the fighting compartment. (US Army)

This M8 from the 4th Cavalry Squadron appears to have everything but the proverbial kitchen sink somewhere on the vehicle. Whitewash has been smeared on the vehicle to help break up its outline (even the mines are camouflaged). Often the side skirts were removed so that mud build-up would not cause problems with the wheels and suspension. A small stowage box has been attached to the rear of the turret. (US Army)

The crew of this M8 point to a statue of Frederick I in the town square of Moere, Germany during the spring of 1945. The hull front is covered with tow and tire chains which provided a little more protection against enemy fire. The turret gunner is holding a 37mm round. (US Army)

A pair of heavily loaded M8s from the 10th Armored Division sit alongside the road in an artillery shredded forest near the city of Wittlich, Germany. Canvas covers over the machine guns and a muzzle cover over the 37mm gun barrel of the second M8 imply the fighting has moved onward. (US Army)

The M8 and M20 saw much more limited use in the Pacific compared to Europe, and was mainly used in the Philippines. The crew of this M8 scan Lebrenan Hill on Leyte for signs of Japanese pillboxes and snipers. The use of the designation 'US ARMY' on the side and rear is unusual in both placement and spelling, especially since there are no registration numbers or vehicle data on the hull side. (US Army)

An American soldier examines an M8 that had been captured and used by the Germans. The name BUFFALO BILL is visible just below the soldier's hand. The Germans have painted over the US insignia and crudely applied over-sized crosses on the hull and turret. There are no identification marks to indicate which US or German unit used the vehicle. (Green)

M8 Turret Gun Mount

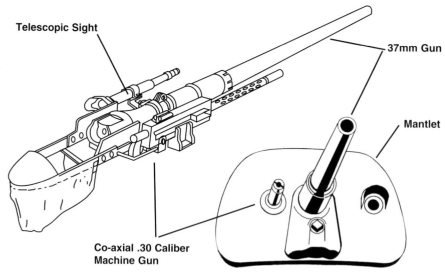

Telescopic Sight

37mm Gun

Mantlet

Co-axial .30 Caliber Machine Gun

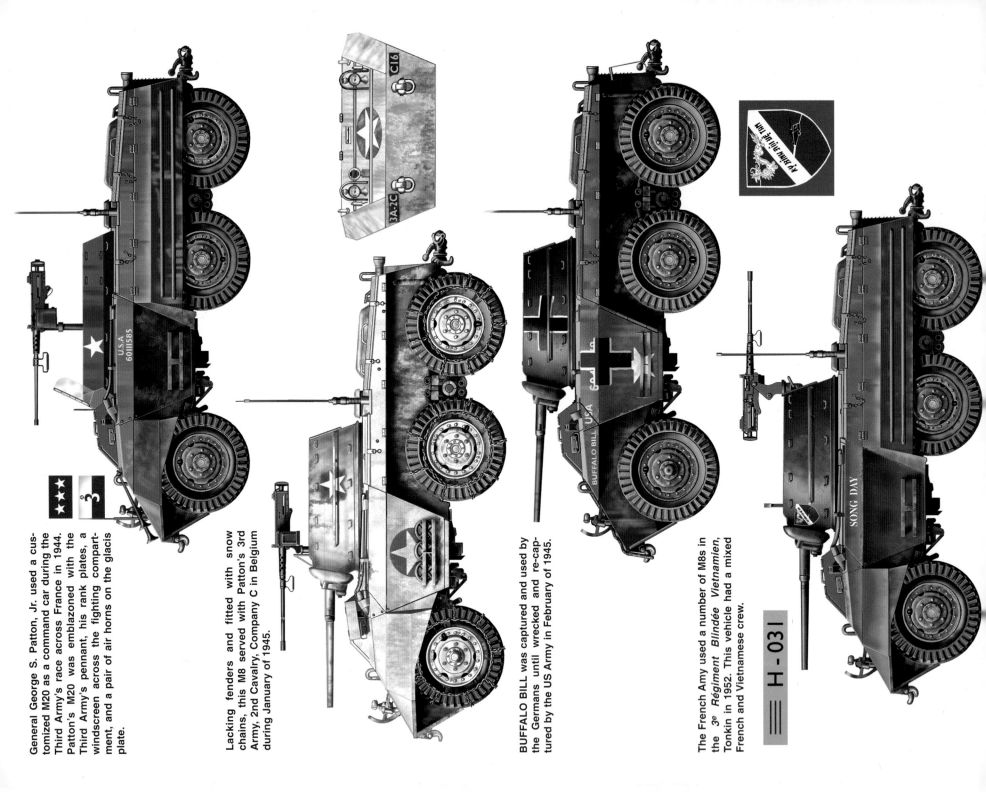

General George S. Patton, Jr. used a customized M20 as a command car during the Third Army's race across France in 1944. Patton's M20 was emblazoned with the Third Army's pennant, his rank plates, a windscreen across the fighting compartment, and a pair of air horns on the glacis plate.

Lacking fenders and fitted with snow chains, this M8 served with Patton's 3rd Army, 2nd Cavalry, Company C in Belgium during January of 1945.

BUFFALO BILL was captured and used by the Germans until wrecked and re-captured by the US Army in February of 1945.

The French Amy used a number of M8s in the 3e Régiment Blindée Vietnamien, Tonkin in 1952. This vehicle had a mixed French and Vietnamese crew.

H - 031

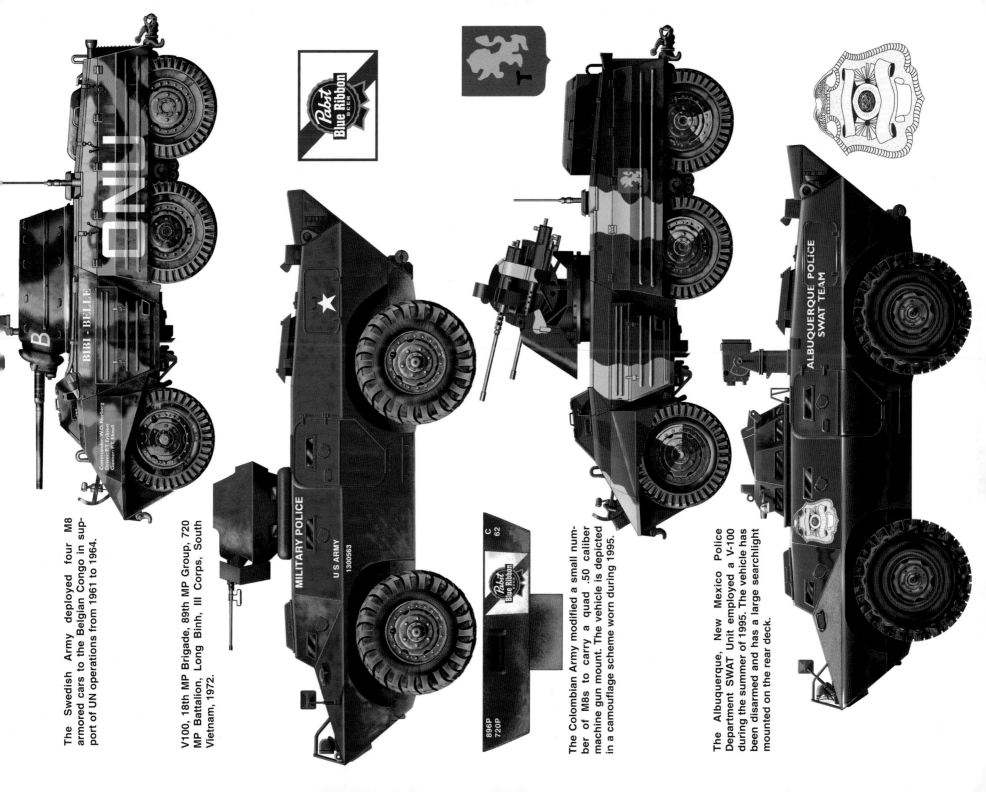

The Swedish Army deployed four M8 armored cars to the Belgian Congo in support of UN operations from 1961 to 1964.

V100, 18th MP Brigade, 89th MP Group, 720 MP Battalion, Long Binh, III Corps, South Vietnam, 1972.

The Colombian Army modified a small number of M8s to carry a quad .50 caliber machine gun mount. The vehicle is depicted in a camouflage scheme worn during 1995.

The Albuquerque, New Mexico Police Department SWAT Unit employed a V-100 during the summer of 1995. The vehicle has been disarmed and has a large searchlight mounted on the rear deck.

UNO

BIBI · BELLE

Commander: W.O. Norberg
Driver: P.T. Erikson
Gunner: P.T. Ekvoll

MILITARY POLICE

U S ARMY
1300563

C
62

896P
720P

ALBUQUERQUE POLICE
SWAT TEAM

Pabst
Blue Ribbon
BEER

Pabst
Blue Ribbon
BEER

A group of US soldiers hitch a ride on board an M8 of the 41st Rescue Troop during March of 1945. The vehicle appears to be backing up along the bank of the Manicahan River on Mindanao. Their casual dress and attitude (and one soldier with a camera) indicates the fighting has likely moved elsewhere. (US Army)

At the end of WW II most US units in Europe were disbanded and returned to the US. A few units, including several Cavalry Squadrons, were redesignated as constabulary units. This M8 is from the 42nd Constabulary Squadron, formerly the 42nd Cavalry Squadron, and was assigned to the 2 Constabulary Regiment in May of 1948. Their insignia, the letter "C" placed on a white disk, earned them the nickname "Circle C Cowboys". (US Army)

An M8 from the 124th Cavalry Regiment prepares to move out of its bivouac area near Lashio, Burma in March of 1945. Assigned to the MARS Task Force, the 124th CR took part in the drive to open the Burma Road below Nankam. The M8 is towing a captured Japanese caisson to carry extra supplies and equipment. (US Army)

US troops were immediately committed to the support of South Korea when hostilities broke out during the summer of 1950. An American M8 of the 8066th Reconnaissance Company, 1st Cavalry Division waits for an ox cart to be moved out of the way. The South Korean Army also had a small number of M8s in their 1st Capital Division. (US Army)

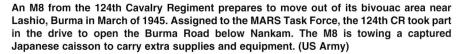

(left) A bare-headed Sgt Raymond A. Cottrell fires on North Koreans soldiers attempting to set up a roadblock in August of 1950. Although the M8 and M20 were useful in roles like this, they were totally outclassed by the North Korean T-34s and were quickly relegated to patrol and security details. (US Army)

(Below Left) While the war raged in Korea, the French were attempting to put down a communist insurgency in Indochina. This M8 is being used against Viet Minh guerrillas during the fighting along the Noire River in January of 1952. The .30 caliber machine gun on the turret ring mount appears to have a spotting light attached to it. (ECPA via Balin)

(Below) As the war in Indochina progressed, the French were forced to create new units using indigenous troops and integrate some of these personnel into their own units. This M8 has a mixed French-Vietnamese crew. The Vietnamese flag — horizontal yellow and red bands — was placed in front of the vehicle's license number on the lower front hull plate. French vehicles carried a French flag and the letters "IC" (for Indochina) in front of the numbers. (ECPA)

T69 Anti-Aircraft Vehicle

Another planned version of the T22/M8 design was as a highly mobile anti-aircraft vehicle. In February of 1943 work began on modifying an M8 to carry a quad .50 machine gun mount in place of the 37mm turret. Testing of the vehicle, designated the T69, ran into 1944 and in general the results were satisfactory. The four machine guns were mounted in a thinly armored turret that rotated through 360 degrees in approximately six seconds. The weapons could be elevated from +90 through -10 degrees and could fire between 1600 to 2000 rounds of ammunition per minute. The speed, range, and mobility of the M8 were not affected by the quad mount. By the time the T69 was ready, the M16 Halftrack — which also mounted a quad .50 caliber machine gun turret and carried more ammunition — was already in production. Since the T69 armored car offered no real improvement over the M16 Halftrack the project was canceled in early 1944.

(Right) The turret could make a complete 360 degree traverse in six seconds. The guns fired at a theoretical rate of 1600 - 2000 rounds per minute, although such a sustained rate of fire was not practical for other than a short period of time due to heat, barrel wear, and ammunition supply. (PAM)

(Below) The guns could elevate between -10 and +90 degrees. Although the T69 had a high road speed and was an effective weapons system, it offered no real improvement over the M16 half-track in terms of firepower, protection, or off-road performance. These factors, and the diminishing threat from Axis air power, led to the termination of the project. (PAM)

(Below) The T69 was an attempt to utilize the M8 in the anti-aircraft role. A power operated open topped turret with four .50 caliber machine guns was fitted in place of the 37mm turret. The ammunition bins were in the base of the turret. Aircraft style chutes fed the rounds to the guns and prevented jamming. (PAM)

T17 Armored Car

In July of 1941 the Ordnance Department issued a requirement for a medium armored car with all-wheel drive and a turret mounted 37mm cannon. Both four and six-wheeled designs were specified and, from the designs submitted, Ford and Chevrolet were each selected to build a prototype. The Ford model featured a six-wheeled layout and was designated the T17. The T17 had a fully traversable 37mm gun turret with a coaxially mounted .30 caliber machine gun. Another .30 caliber machine gun was mounted in the hull to the right of the driver. A third .30 caliber weapon was mounted on a pintle on the turret. Power was supplied by a 320 cubic inch Hercules JXD engine which gave the eleven ton T17 an open road speed of 60 MPH. The five-man crew gained entry through hatches in the hull side behind the front wheels and hatches in the open topped turret. Storage boxes ran the entire length of the vehicle on both sides of the fenders.

Following successful testing, a contract was awarded to Ford in January of 1942 for 2260 T17s. An additional 1500 vehicles were ordered in June of the same year and a production line was set up at the Ford plant in St Paul, Minnesota. In October of 1942, however, the Armored Vehicle Board convened and began a thorough examination of the various armored vehicle projects then underway. Due to the size and weight of the vehicle — almost as much as a light tank — the T17 program was canceled. However, as the T22/M8 had been accepted for production, Ford was allowed to complete the first 250 T17s in order to keep the production line open. The vehicles were offered to the British who had already named the vehicle 'Deerhound', but they declined due to an adequate supply of what they considered superior vehicles. Ironically, it was British experience, requirements, and input which led to the excessive size and weight and subsequently the two reasons that led to the T17's cancellation. The 250 completed vehicles were redesignated the M5 Armored Car, stripped of their weapons, and assigned to military police (MP) units at bases in the US for patrol and security work. None ever saw combat in the war zones.

(Below and Below Left) The T17 was a large vehicle using a 37mm gun, two engines, and a five-man crew. Entry into the vehicle was usually through the large side hatches behind the front wheels and hatches on the turret roof. In addition to the main gun, there was a co-axially mounted .30 caliber machine gun in the turret, another in the bow plate, and provision for a third on top of the turret. Stowage boxes ran the length of the fenders. (PAM)

T17E1 Armored Car

The Chevrolet design for a medium armored car was a four-wheeled vehicle designated the T17E1. The British were again the main force in drawing up the requirements for the vehicle based on their needs and battlefield experience. The pilot model was completed in late 1941 and test results were satisfactory. An initial order for 2000 vehicles was placed with 300 being allocated to the British under Lend-Lease. The British named the vehicle 'Staghound'. Like the T17 the Armored Vehicle Board decided that the T17E1 was not needed by American forces, but the British felt the vehicle fit their requirements. Consequently it was decided to build the vehicle exclusively for the British Army. Eventually 2844 units were produced.

At fifteen tons, the Staghound was a relatively heavy vehicle for an armored car. It was powered by two 97 horsepower GMC Model 270 engines mounted side-by-side in the rear compartment. The Staghound's four wheel drive provided good off-road performance and a normal road speed of about 55 MPH. The 112 gallon fuel capacity provided a range of 200 to 500 miles depending on the terrain. Two additional fuel tanks were mounted on either side of the hull and could be jettisoned from inside the vehicle if necessary.

The crew of five consisted of the driver and assistant driver in the hull and the commander, gunner, and loader in the turret. Entry into the Staghound was through hatches on either side of the hull in front of the jettisonable fuel tanks, through hatches over the driver and his assistant, or via the commander's and gunner's hatches in the turret roof.

The vehicle was armed with a 37mm cannon in an M6 mount with a coaxial .30 caliber machine gun. Another .30 caliber machine gun was fitted to the right side of the hull and operated by the assistant driver. There was also provision for a pintle mounted .30 machine gun on top of the turret. Approximately 100 rounds of 37mm ammunition was carried along with 5000 rounds of .30 caliber ammunition. The turret was hydraulically traversed while the gun was elevated using a hand wheel. A gyrostabilizer was tied into the gun to allow more accurate aiming while on the move. While the 37mm gun no longer had the necessary power to engage German armor, the combination of armor (in some places two inches thick), speed, and off-road capability made the vehicle useful in the British armored car regiments. The units in Italy were especially glad to receive the Staghound to replace their more outdated equipment. Apart from a few that may have been tested at the US Army's Desert Warfare School, the entire order was assigned to the British and other Commonwealth units in Europe. The US eventually

designated the T17E1 the M6, but since the vehicle did not see service in US Army, the designation was rarely used.

Variants

The Staghound had enough versatility to allow other vehicles to be developed from the basic design. The first was the T17E2 anti-aircraft vehicle which carried an open-topped Frazer-Nash turret in lieu of the 37mm turret. The power operated turret was armed with a pair of .50 caliber machine guns and could traverse through 360 degrees in about seven seconds. Each of the guns could fire about 600 rounds per minute. Since the turret weapons could be used against ground targets, the bow machine gun and the assistant driver were eliminated. The crew was reduced to the driver, an ammunition handler in the hull, and the commander/gunner in the turret. Additional radio equipment was fitted into the hull area formerly occupied by the assistant driver.

The second variant was the T17E3. The standard Staghound hull was fitted with a complete turret and 75mm howitzer from the M8 Howitzer Motor Carriage (a self-propelled gun based on the M5 Stuart hull and running gear). Only one pilot model was completed before the project was terminated in December of 1943.

The third model was the Staghound III which had the original 37mm turret replaced with the complete turret from a Crusader III tank. The turret mounted an M3 75mm gun which gave the Staghound III a degree of firepower well beyond its size. Nevertheless, this was solely a British project and only a small number were converted. Like the Staghound AA version, the bow machine gun was deleted. The jettisonable fuel tanks were also eliminated and replaced by large storage boxes.

The final variant, again a strictly British conversion, was the Staghound Command Vehicle. The vehicles were usually modified simply by removing the turret and adding additional radios and map tables. Since this conversion was carried out at the field level, the degree (and perhaps quality) of the work varied. Some vehicles had a windscreen or metal shield in front of the turret ring or a fold-down canvas top. Like the Staghound III, only a small number of vehicles were so modified.

T17E1 (Staghound)

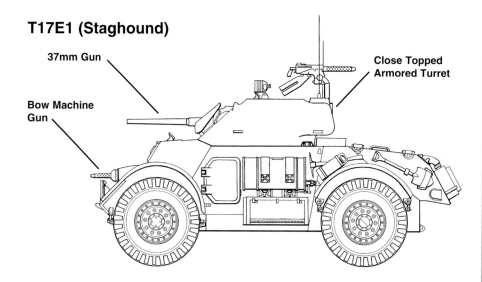

- 37mm Gun
- Bow Machine Gun
- Close Topped Armored Turret

The T17E1 resembled a shortened version of the T17, sharing the same turret, two engines, and side access hatches. However, the shortened wheel base, four wheels, and rounded fenders made it easy to see the differences. The similarities resulted from the same specifications issued for two vehicle designs — one with four wheels and one with six wheels. (PAM)

The T17E1 or Staghound was a straightforward design with a box-shaped hull and a simplified steering and transmission system which was based on Chrysler types used on automobiles prior to the war. The fuel drums on the sides were jettisonable from inside the hull. While not used by US forces, the Staghound proved very popular with British and Commonwealth forces in Europe. (PAM)

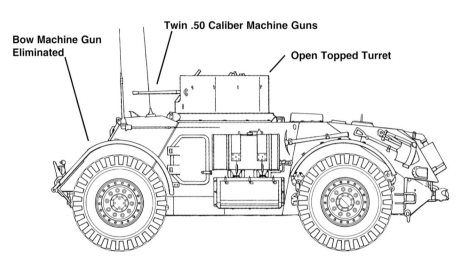

T17E2 Anti-Aircraft Vehicle

Bow Machine Gun Eliminated

Twin .50 Caliber Machine Guns

Open Topped Turret

The T17E1 hull was used as the basis for the T17E2 anti-aircraft vehicle. The vehicle used a pair of .50 caliber machine guns mounted in an open topped Frazer-Nash power turret. A ring-and-bead sight was used to aim the weapons. (PAM)

The turret could traverse in about seven seconds and had a rate of fire of around 600 rounds per minute. The bow machine gun was eliminated since the turret weapons could also be used against ground targets. The crew was reduced to three men and the additional space was used for radio gear and ammunition storage. (PAM)

The T17E3 was designed as a close support vehicle and featured a 75mm howitzer in the open topped turret of the M8 Howitzer Motor Carriage (HMC). The vehicle never went into production, but eventually the British modified some Staghounds with the turret and 75mm gun from the Crusader III tank under the name of Staghound III. Other Staghounds had their 37mm gun replaced by a three inch howitzer under the designation Staghound II. (PAM)

(Above) A group of Canadian 4th Armoured Division Staghounds crosses a Bailey Bridge over the Seine River during the late summer of 1944. The crew of the lead vehicle has used the gap between the fenders for additional storage atop the standard hull storage box. (Canadian Public Archives)

(Below) Several months later, in early March of 1945, a column of Staghounds and other vehicles from the Canadian 4th Armoured Division moves along a dirt road near the town of Sonsbeck, Germany. The Staghound was well liked for its heavy armor protection, although its size could be a tactical hindrance in certain circumstances. (Canadian Public Archives)

T18/T18E2 Armored Car

The July 1941 Ordnance Department requirements that led to the T17 and T17E1 also drove the request for six or eight wheeled heavy armored cars. The proposals were to have the same fully traversable, closed topped 37mm turret as the T17. General Motor's Yellow Truck and Coach Division submitted a design and two eight-wheeled prototypes were ordered under the designation T18. An alternative, the six-wheeled T18E1, was also ordered with independent springs for each wheel. As with the T18, two vehicles were ordered. Eventually, it was decided to produce only one of each version and work proceeded accordingly. Work on the T18E1 was eventually stopped due to the development of a similar design, the T19.

Following testing, a tentative order for 2500 T18 armored cars was placed in early 1942. However, the British Tank Mission stepped in during the spring of 1942 and requested changes in the design, primarily in the armament. British combat experience in North Africa had shown the increasing obsolescence of the 37mm gun and they felt a heavier weapon was needed. They wanted a six pound gun in place of the 37mm weapon. The new gun required the design of a larger turret. Since this weapon was to be produced in the US as the 57mm cannon, no serious problems were expected. The modified vehicle was redesignated the T18E2 and an additional 300 were ordered in March.

The eight-wheeled T18E2 was a large vehicle — over twenty feet long and weighing over twenty-six tons — placing it between the M24 Light Tank and the M4 Sherman Medium Tank. The hull was of welded construction with a cast nose and turret. The crew consisted of the driver, assistant driver, gunner, loader and commander. Hatches in the hull sides, over the driver's and assistant driver's compartments, and over the commander and gunner in the turret roof provided access to the vehicle. The vehicle was powered by two 125 HP, six-cylinder Chevrolet engines driving all eight wheels. Both front axles were used for steering. Two jettisonable fuel tanks were mounted at the rear, but the range was still limited to about 250 miles under optimum conditions.

The T18E2 was the largest US armored car built during WW II. It had a new, fully enclosed turret with a 57mm gun, but otherwise differed little from the earlier T18. The new gun gave the Boarhound a heavier punch, but the sheer size of the vehicle made it very conspicuous. Only thirty were produced — all going to the British. (PAM)

The main armament was a 57mm cannon in a fully traversable, hydraulically powered closed topped turret. A .30 caliber machine gun was mounted co-axially with the main gun and there was a flexibly mounted .30 caliber weapon in the right hull fired by the assistant driver. It does not appear that there were initially provisions for a pintle mounted .30 caliber machine gun on the turret, but if large scale production had taken place, this probably would have been added. There were also provisions for a turret-mounted two-inch smoke bomb thrower.

Unfortunately, the T18E2, named the 'Boarhound' by the British, ran into problems from the very start of the program. The sheer size of the Boarhound made tooling up for production take longer than anticipated. Additionally, delivery of the 57mm guns lagged behind due to production delays. When the Armored Vehicle Board convened in the fall of 1942 the T18E2 fell under its scrutiny. While the Boarhound was well armed and armored, its overall size and high silhouette made it tactically unsuitable for its mission. Coupled with poor cross country mobility, there were other vehicles, both tanks and armored cars, which provided more flexibility than the T18E2. By November the Board dropped the requirements for the T18E2 stating it was simply too large for American use. Cancellation of the program allowed resources to be shifted to programs that showed more promise. Due to the efforts that had already gone into tooling and setting up the production line, however, it was decided to complete 30 vehicles to meet British requirements. However, the need for such a large armored car had disappeared — if there had ever been a need in the first place — and none of the Boarhounds were ever used in combat.

In retrospect, the requirements which led to the Boarhound were probably unrealistic in light of the eventual development of other vehicles. At the time, however, the Ordnance Department was trying to cover all contingencies. Later, when the Armor Board was able to evaluate the program under calmer conditions, it had the good sense to cancel the project.

T18E2 Boarhound

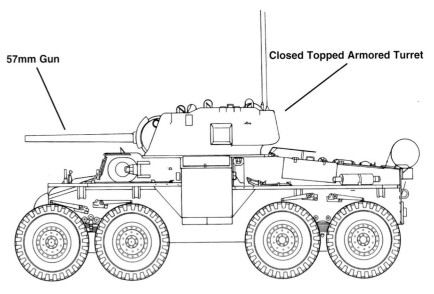

57mm Gun

Closed Topped Armored Turret

Like the Staghound, the Boarhound was equipped with jettisonable fuel tanks, although these were located at the rear. Entry into the vehicle was excellent, with side and upper hatches for the driver's compartment, and two in the turret roof. Although well-armed and armored, the British only used the Boarhound in tests and it was declared obsolete in January of 1944. One surviving vehicle is on display at the Tank Museum at Bovington Camp in the United Kingdom. (PAM)

The T19 was similar to the Boarhound although it only had six wheels on a shorter hull. The prototype was only partially completed before work shifted to the extensively modified second prototype. The T19 was armed with a 37mm gun, although it had been removed when this photo was taken. Of interest are the large springs used in the suspension. (PAM)

T19/T66 Armored Car

While the T18E1 was under development, work began in January of 1942 on the similar T19. As the T19 design progressed, its superiority over the T18E1 became apparent and work on the T18E1 was halted. Two T19 prototypes were ordered. The first prototype bore a close resemblance to the T18, however, the weight and height were deemed excessive. The second T19 prototype was given a smaller 37mm turret and had its overall height and weight reduced. The vehicle subsequently received the new designation T19E1. The Tank Destroyer Command saw the vehicle and asked if the 37mm turret could be replaced with a new open-topped turret fitted with a 75mm gun. Chevrolet worked on this request, resulting in a new vehicle — the T66 75mm Gun Motor Carriage.

However, the Armor Board, in reviewing all three vehicles during the fall of 1942, concluded that while basically sound designs, their development was not warranted since there was little, if any, future requirement for them. US Army mechanized doctrine was rapidly evolving and combat experience had amply demonstrated the obsolescence of the 37mm gun as an anti-tank weapon. Even the 57mm was approaching the end of its developmental life as German armor grew larger and more powerful. To mount larger weapons on armored cars would have required larger, heavier vehicles with thicker armor. Conceptually, this was moving well beyond what Army planners envisioned as a role for the armored car — a light fast vehicle used for deep reconnaissance. Work on all three vehicles was terminated at the end of 1942.

The second prototype featured a new turret and revised hull to reduce its height and weight. It was designated the T19E1 and retained the T19's 37mm gun and co-axial .30 caliber machine gun. Another .30 caliber weapon was mounted in the glacis plate. (PAM)

T27 Heavy Armored Car

In January of 1943 the Special Armored Vehicle Board issued new requirements for future armored cars that resulted in two new designs being submitted. The Studebaker Company submitted a seven ton, eight-wheeled design designated T27. All eight wheels were evenly spaced — a feature rarely seen on eight-wheeled armored car designs. Additionally, all of the wheels were individually sprung using a torsion bar suspension and the rear six wheels were powered. The vehicle was equipped with an opened topped 37mm turret and, overall, its outline bore a strong resemblance to the M8. When completed in early 1944, the T27 was tested against the equally new T28 and an M8. Although an elegant and capable vehicle, test results showed that the T27 was inferior to the T28 and it offered no significant advantage over the production M8. Since the T28 was a better vehicle and there were significant numbers of M8s already on hand and in production, the T27 program was canceled in July of 1944.

Fitted with chains on its wheels, the T19E1 negotiates a muddy river bank during one of its tests. Although the T19E1 performed well during testing, it was still too heavy. (PAM)

While the T19E1 was being tested the Tank Destroyer Command requested the vehicle be fitted with a 75mm gun for use as a wheeled tank destroyer. An open-topped turret was developed to replace the 37mm unit and the new vehicle was designated the T66, 75mm Gun Motor Carriage. (PAM)

The T27 came about as a result of new requirements issued by the Special Armored Vehicle Board in early 1943. Studebaker's design featured eight wheels (six of which were powered) and was armed with a 37mm gun. The requirement for the 37mm gun would seem rather odd in light of the weapon's obsolescence. In retrospect, the larger 57mm gun would seem to have been a more logical choice for such a large vehicle even though it too was seeing the end of its useful life. (PAM)

(Below) The torsion bar suspension allowed the T27 to move over uneven ground with comparative ease. However, the wheels could move quite high up on the hull side and care had to be taken when going over rough terrain. During testing the T27 was found to be inferior to the six-wheeled T28 and the project was canceled in mid-1944. (PAM)

(Above) There was also a co-axial .30 caliber machine gun mounted in the T27's turret. The gun turret had a large stowage bustle on the rear, but was otherwise similar to the M8's turret. Additional stowage boxes were mounted on the fenders over the middle pair of wheels. (PAM)

(Below) The T27 was one of the few eight-wheeled armored cars which had evenly spaced wheels. Weighing a little over seven tons, the vehicle had a good distribution of weight over the entire frame. There was no bow machine gun although there were provisions for a .30 caliber machine gun mounted on top of the turret. (PAM)

T28/M38 Armored Car

M38 Wolfhound

Chevrolet submitted the second design under the new requirements issued in early 1943. The six-wheeled vehicle showed a great deal of potential. Its coil spring suspension, equally spaced wheels, and high power-to-weight ratio gave it excellent cross country performance. The T28 also featured sloping armor which improved its ballistic protection and reduced the vehicle's overall weight. Armed with a 37mm gun in an opened topped turret, the seven and one-half ton vehicle had a top speed of 60 MPH and a range of 300 miles. Power was supplied by a Chevrolet Cadillac V8 engine.

When tested against the T27 and M8 in the spring of 1944, the T28 proved superior to both vehicles. As a result, the T28 was redesignated M38 and ordered into production in late 1944 as a replacement for the M8. Before production could begin, however, the program was canceled when it was realized the end of the war was near and there were sufficient M8s on hand to handle any future requirements.

The M38 was probably the best US designed armored car of the war. In British service, it was to have been known as the 'Wolfhound'. It is interesting to speculate what would have happened had the M38 actually become operational. In fact many elements of its design did see service in the post-war British Saladin armored car. The Saladin bears more than a passing resemblance to the M38 in its suspension, wheel base, and general outline.

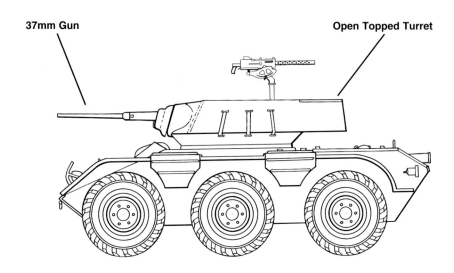

37mm Gun   Open Topped Turret

The Special Armored Vehicle Board requirements which brought about the T27 also resulted in the six-wheeled T28. Although similar in size to the M8, the T28 was a far superior vehicle with better cross-country performance, armor protection, and a higher speed. The T28 carried the same 37mm cannon, but in a larger turret. (PAM)

The T28 moves down a road followed by the T27 during its test program. The T28 was also tested against the M8 and found to be superior to both vehicles. This led to the cancellation of the T27 and replacement of the M8 with the T28 (redesignated the M38). However, the end of the war and a surplus of M8s resulted in the cancellation of the M38. (PAM)

After the war, the M38 was fitted with the turret from an M24 Chaffee light tank. While the new turret mounted 75mm gun gave the M38 a tremendous upgrade in firepower, the increased weight reduced its overall performance. (PAM)

V-100 Commando

Following World War Two, US Army interest in armored cars quickly waned. During the Korean War some M8s and M20s were used for a variety of security duties, but there was no serious interest in, or need for, a new series of armored cars. The Army preferred to rely on light tanks and Armored Personnel Carriers (APCs) for security and reconnaissance duties. Additionally, the US Army was focused on the possibility of a major war with the Soviet Union in central Europe and it was felt that armored cars would be of little use. Unfortunately, while the Army concentrated on Europe, American foreign policy led to an involvement in Vietnam. By the mid-1960s US forces were deeply involved in the fighting in South Vietnam and the lack of a mobile wheeled vehicle for road and convoy security was suddenly and acutely felt.

At the time the firm of Cadillac Gage had a new, privately developed vehicle which offered an answer to the problem — the V-100 Commando. The V-100's design came about when the company realized there was a need, and hence a market, for a special purpose, wheeled vehicle which featured a simple design and upkeep. Cadillac Gage came up with a four-wheeled vehicle, about the size of a truck, which had an angular hull for optimum ballistic protection and a variety of armament options. The armament options allowed the V-100 to be tailored for a variety of missions while still using the same basic hull and drive train.

The V-100 design began in the early 1960s when Cadillac Gage experimented with a Dodge truck fitted with an armored body. This was followed by the V-100 prototype which was built in March of 1963. The hallmark of the V-100 was the angular design of its hull armor. Homogeneous ballistic plates were welded in such a fashion to provide maximum deflection against small arms fire (up to 7.62mm) and other light ordnance including grenades, shrapnel, and anti-personnel mines.

The M38, named Wolfhound by the British, was a fine design and probably the best of its type, but the end of the war and abundance of M8s could not justify putting it into production. The post war British Saladin armored car bore a strong resemblance to the M38. (PAM)

After WW II there was little official interest in armored car development and, with later US involvement in Vietnam, the lack of a suitable armored car became evident. Fortunately, the Cadillac-Gage Company had developed the V-100 Commando as a private venture. This is one of the early vehicles with periscopes. Later production vehicles would have vision ports in their place. (PAM)

The eight-ton V-100 was powered by a Chrysler 361 gasoline engine which, with a five speed manual transmission, had a road speed of over 60 MPH. The four wheels, all powered, were mounted on modified M34 truck axles. The tires were the special "run flat" combat type of 12 reinforced steel ply that could be driven up to 50 miles after being pierced by gunfire. Each wheel used leaf springs and full shock absorbers to provide a smooth ride over rough ground. A particular design feature was the high road clearance which allowed the V-100 to go over large obstacles as well as lessening the effects of mines. The drive train was fitted inside the hull for better protection. After minor preparation, the V-100 was fully amphibious on relatively calm bodies of water. The wheels propelled the vehicle in water at a maximum speed of 3.5 MPH. The vehicle was also equipped with a 10,000 pound capacity hydraulic winch on the hull front.

The crew of the V100 consisted of four men: the driver, gunner, radio operator and commander. Access to the vehicle was quite good with three main doors on the hull — two on each side and one in the hull rear to the right of the engine. All three doors were built in two parts with the lower section folding down. The upper section of the rear door hinged upward, while the upper sections of the side doors hinged to the side. Three additional hatches were placed on the hull top: one each over the driver and radio operator and one on the rear deck just in front of the rear hull hatch. While the first V-100s featured periscopes, later vehicles were fitted with vision blocks — two in front, four on the right side, three on the left and one in the rear. The vision blocks on the sides and rear were each paired with a firing port. On the front a single firing port was located between the driver's and radio operator's vision blocks.

While the armament of the V-100 varied from model to model, the V-100s used by the Army in Vietnam under the designation XM706/M706, featured a small armored cupola with a single hatch, eight vision blocks, and twin .30 caliber machine guns. Some vehicles were equipped with a turret mounted .30 and .50 caliber weapon. A second version used by the Air Force was designated the XM706E2. It dispensed with the turret and featured an open top sur-

rounded by an armored parapet behind the driver's compartment. The parapet was equipped with pintle mounts for machine guns.

The initial batch of US Army V-100s procured for service in Vietnam in 1966 were designated XM706s. Following their trials, the decision was made to buy additional vehicles with only minor modifications. These included revised hatches over the driver and radio operator and the addition of a shield over the top of the engine grill. The revised vehicles were redesignated the M706 and used by both US and ARVN (Army of the Republic of Vietnam) forces for convoy duty and perimeter security.

The need to protect convoys against attacks had become a serious problem as the fighting in South Vietnam escalated and the US troop commitment grew. In 1966 an initial batch of V100/XM706 vehicles was shipped to Vietnam for testing. Aside from minor modifications, the new armored car proved satisfactory and more were ordered for use by the Army, Air Force, and ARVN forces. The Commando proved to be an excellent response for a fast vehicle to keep pace with trucks, something which armor could not do. The M706s also had sufficient firepower to repel attacks and enough protection to survive against most small arms and shrapnel. Used by various Military Police (MP) units for road and base security, the M706s, sometimes called 'Vs' or 'Ducks' due to their pointed nose, served throughout the country until the American troop withdrawal in 1973. Many of the remaining vehicles were turned over to the South Vietnamese who used them in a similar role. Later, many of these were captured when South Vietnam fell to the invading North in the spring of 1975. Some of these vehicles were, in turn, used by the North Vietnamese when they invaded Cambodia. Although some may still be in use, the lack of spare parts has probably resulted in most of them being con-

The angular, sloping hull of the V-100 provided excellent ballistic protection from small arms fire. Access was excellent, with a total of seven hatches in the hull and turret. This vehicle is equipped with a single .50 caliber machine gun and a .30 caliber weapon in the turret. Most vehicles were not fitted with turret mounted smoke mortars. (PAM)

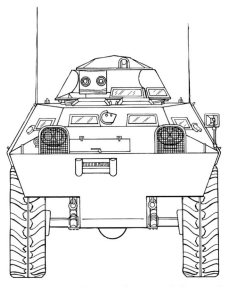

V-100 Armored Car Specifications

Length...........18 Feet, 8 Inches
Width..............7 Feet, 5 Inches
Height.............8 Feet
Weight............16,250 Pounds
Armament.......2 x .30 Caliber Machine Guns, or 2 x 7.62mm
                Machine Guns, or 1 x .30 Cal MG and 1 x .50
                Cal MG
Speed............62 MPH (3.5 MPH in Water)
Crew..............3-4

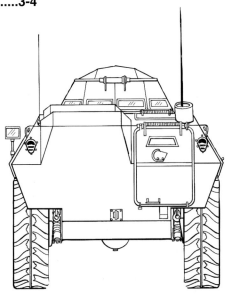

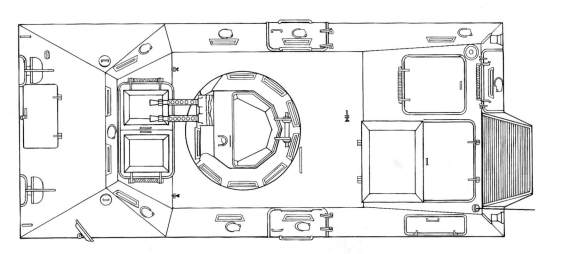

signed to the scrap heap.

The V-100 proved to be a successful commercial venture for Cadillac Gage. As a result, the company embarked on a new series of designs based on the V-100. The first of these was the V200, a heavier vehicle introduced in 1969. The vehicle fared poorly in the market due to its increased cost and complexity when compared to the V-100. Cadillac Gage then decided to simply improve the basic V-100 design. This resulted in the introduction of the V-150 in 1971. Bearing a strong resemblance to its predecessor, it was designed to carry a variety of armament packages and powered turrets mounting guns up to 90mm. Over 20 different configurations were available and the V-150 proved to be the best commercial sales model of the series with over 4000 manufactured. Another variant, the V-150S, was started in 1981. The vehicle featured a lengthened body that allowed the fitting of additional weapons packages.

In 1979 Cadillac Gage introduced the larger, six-wheeled V-300 design which broke the pattern of the earlier four-wheeled V-100, V-150, and V-200. Building on the basics of the earlier versions, the V-300 also featured a wide variety of armament packages. The increase in size allowed the engine to be moved to the front of the vehicle which, in turn, cleared space for a larger, two part hatch at the vehicle's rear for rapid troop deployment.

In 1994 Cadillac Gage merged with Textron Marine Systems to form Textron Marine and Land Systems. The new company then introduced the LAV-600 which featured a 105mm low recoil gun system. There was also a redesignation of the series to Light Armored Vehicles (LAV) to better describe the vehicles. The increase in firepower and weight changed the new series from armored cars, as the V-100 was, to a new class of armored vehicles as the name indicates. Aside from the V-100/M706, none of these vehicles were used by American forces although the number of foreign nations using the vehicles has grown to over two dozen. In some ways, the US has come full circle since the late 1930s. While the US has shown little interest in armored cars, their development in America has not lapsed. Should the need arise, as it did in Vietnam, there is an industry and in-place production capacity to quickly provide the US armed forces with such vehicles.

Lesser known is the use of modified M8s, M20s, and V-100s by the police departments of several American cities. In all cases the heavy weapons were removed and in Detroit, the old 37mm turret was modified with vision ports and a cupola. Some saw service during the riots that swept several major US cities in the 1960s. Over the years a number of V100s have been purchased for use by police Special Weapons and Tactics (SWAT) Teams and used in areas of high drug, hostage, or gang related violence. The vehicles have enough protection to withstand a high volume of counter fire that has become a problem for some law enforcement officials, yet still remain compatible with the police mission. Of equal importance, their off-road capability means they are not restricted to paved roads and can move about with impunity — something the standard police cruiser may not be able to do. The downsizing of the military also means many vehicles, parts, and expertise are widely available at low cost. Although most violent crime in America has spiraled downward, more police departments may acquire such vehicles to bolster their crowd control, SWAT, and hostage rescue units.

The primary purpose of the armored car in the US Army had been reconnaissance. Modern electronics, unmanned aerial reconnaissance vehicles, and satellites with real-time reporting capabilities have rendered the armored car's original mission largely obsolete. Additionally, the increasing range and lethality of small arms and light anti-armor weapons have made the lighter armored vehicles increasingly vulnerable as well, even in low-intensity Third World conflicts. The vehicles designed to replace the traditional armored cars have grown larger and heavier as a result. Vehicles such as the Cadillac Gage Ranger/Peacekeeper and Scout, the Dragoon 300 series, and the LAV25 series by General Motors now fall outside what would be the original definition of armored cars. The current lack of official interest in the traditional armored car may indeed be simply a realization that such a vehicle may not have a mission on today's modern battlefield. Nevertheless, with the global American military commitment, the majority of which involves the low-keyed use of military force, the Light Armored Vehicle family now emerging is the logical successor to the armored car legacy.

The V-300 used the earlier Commando series as a starting point, but went to a six-wheeled configuration and moved the engine from the rear to the front. It also carried a variety of different turrets and had twin exit doors at the rear. The vehicle's size and armament have taken the design beyond that of the traditional armored car. (Cadillac Gage/Textron)

The larger and more powerful LAV-600 followed the V-300, which really put the vehicle out of the armored car class. The LAV-600 mounts a new, low recoil 105mm gun, giving it far superior firepower over the earlier vehicles. It is still fairly lightweight when compared to modern tanks. (Cadillac Gage/Textron)

The V-150 was an improved version of the V-100 designed to carry a more powerful armament in an enlarged turret. This model carries a 20mm cannon in the turret. Another turret was able to carry a 90mm low recoil gun. Altogether there were over 20 different models available — all using the same basic chassis. Ultimately, the V-150 was the most successful of the Commando line. (PAM)

The V-100's tires are a 12 ply reinforced steel and were designed to run for 50 miles after being punctured by small arms fire or shrapnel. The tires can also propel the vehicle in water up to a speed of 3.5 MPH. (Mesko)

The V-100 is equipped with a 10,000 pound capacity winch. A hatch on the front deck provides access. The cable has been removed exposing the winch drum. (Mesko)

Access to the interior was normally gained through the side or rear hatches. The bottom section hinged downward and was used as a step, while the upper section was hinged to the side. The side hatch at the rear of the vehicle provided additional access to the engine compartment. (Mesko)

Access to the driver's position was through a set of hatches on top of the hull. Early V-100s had flat hatches while later models were fitted with bulged hatches to increase the drivers' headroom while wearing helmets and headphones. The changes resulted from data sent back from Vietnam. (Mesko)

Each hatch swung outward, exposing the whole compartment. A pad was attached to the top of the hatch to help protect the driver's head when the hatch was closed. The spring between the hinges counterbalanced the weight of the hatch. (Mesko)

The rear deck had hatches for both the interior and the engine. The engine hatch is built in two sections, with the vented front section covered by a shield — another modification as a result of early experience in Vietnam. The grill at the back vents engine and radiator heat and was normally covered with a raised plate. The circular cups are shields for the bases of the radio antennas. (Mesko)

Unlike the bulged drivers' hatches, the rear deck hatch was flat. A rubber water seal was fitted around the rim of the hatch opening. There were also provisions for mounting machine guns on the rear deck at this position. (Mesko)

44

Twin .30 Machine Gun Turret

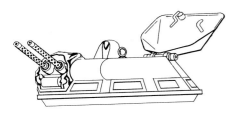

One .30 Caliber Machine Gun and One .50 Caliber Machine Gun Turret

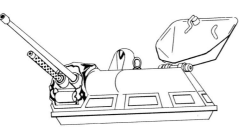

Vision ports were provided all around the turret edge, giving the commander an excellent field of view. The turret hatch was also bulged to provide extra headroom. This particular vehicle is one slightly modified by the Albuquerque Police Department for their SWAT unit. (Mesko)

Access through the rear was through a similar hatch arrangement although in this case the upper hatch section swung upward. A vision block was incorporated into the upper section of the hatch. The bottom hatch also served as a step. (Mesko)

Both the rear hull hatch and the upper hull hatch were in the right rear corner of the V-100. The engine compartment is on the vehicle's left side and is equipped with several removable panels. (Mesko)

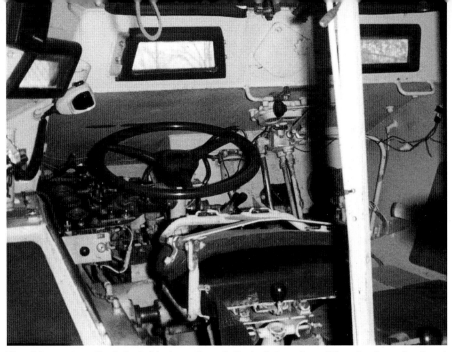

The driver sat on the left. Aside from the relatively flat angles of the steering wheel and instrument panel, the layout of the driver's position was conventional. The back side of the firing port and its serrated locking knob is barely visible between the front vision blocks. The driver's seat back is folded down. (Mesko)

The center and left rear section of the fighting compartment houses the engine bay and a small niche for a fire extinguisher. The port side crew entry hatch is to the right. (Mesko)

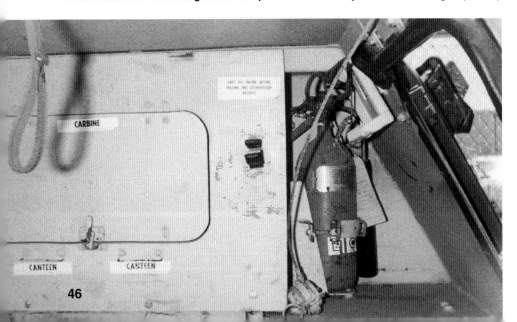

Vision Block and Firing Port (Interior)

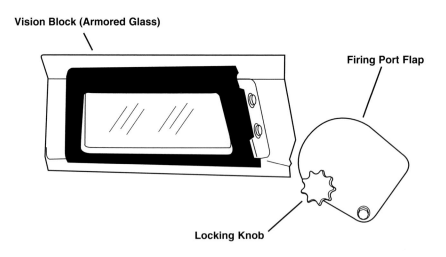

The V-100 was powered by a Chrysler 361 gasoline engine similar to the one used in the M113 Armored Personnel Carrier. The radiator header tank is at the front of the engine bay with the generator on the right. The air cleaner is directly under the radiator tank. (Mesko)

Surplus armored cars have found their way into the police forces of several US cities. This V-100 with an added searchlight on the rear deck is in use by the Albuquerque, New Mexico SWAT team. Sergeant Joel Block was instrumental in letting the author photograph this V-100 of the Albuquerque PD. (Mesko)

The hatch covering the drive train has been removed, allowing access to the transmission and transfer case from inside the vehicle. The armored floor shielded many of the vital drive train components from the effects of mines. (Mesko)

(Left) The other V-100 variant put into service by the US military was the XM706E2 which had the turret replaced with an open topped fighting compartment with armored sides — in some ways similar to the M20. The vehicle was used by the USAF as a perimeter security vehicle at various installations in Vietnam. From photographic evidence it appears the vehicles were normally camouflaged in the three colors used on aircraft — tan and two shades of green. This vehicle is on patrol along the perimeter of Binh Thuy airfield in the IV Corps region, southwest of Saigon. (USAF)

(Below) After US forces were committed to the fighting in Vietnam in the mid-1960s, heavily laden convoys became prime targets for Viet Cong ambushes. Cadillac Gage's privately developed V-100 armored car fit the requirement for a light, fast, well armed and armored vehicle to help protect the convoys. The crews of these V-100s take a break during the trip to An Khe in the Central Highlands. They are with an MP Company of the 4th Infantry Division. (US Army)

(Right) A V-100 of the 16th Military Police Group, 93rd Military Police Battalion leads a convoy along a road near Qui Nhon in South Vietnam. Many MP crews painted colorful markings on the lower bow plate, with cartoon characters being particularly popular. Wire mesh screens protect the headlights. (US Army)

(Below) The arrival of the first Boeing 747 in Vietnam was cause for increased security. A camouflaged USAF V-100 sits in the shadow of the big 747 while baggage is unloaded at Tan Son Nhut Air Base in July of 1971. Two M60 machine guns have been mounted on either side of the parapet as the crew scans the area for any signs of trouble. (USAF)

49

2012 PzKpfw IV

2016 Sherman

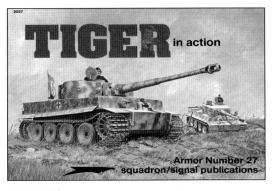

2027 Tiger

2030 M2/M3 Bradley

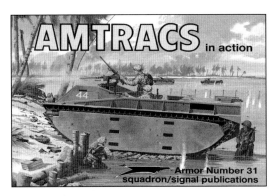

2031 AMTRACS

2033 M3 Lee/Grant

2034 M3 Half-Track

2035 DUKW

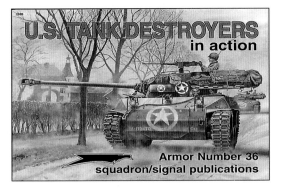

2036 US Tank Destroyers